play guitar with

pop anthems

Wise Publications
London/New York/Paris/Sydney/Copenhagen/Madrid/Tokyo

Music Sales Limited
8-9 Frith Street,
London W1V 5TZ, England.

Music Sales Pty Limited
120 Rothschild Avenue,
Rosebery, NSW 2018, Australia.

Order No. AM960982
ISBN 0-7119-7866-2
This book © Copyright 2000
by Wise Publications

Music compiled and arranged by Arthur Dick
Music processed by Andrew Shiels
Cover photographs courtesy of Retna

Printed in the United Kingdom by
Caligraving Limited, Thetford, Norfolk.

CD programmed by John Moores
Recorded by Kester Sims
Guitar preparation by Charlie Chandler at Chandler Guitars
All guitars by Arthur Dick
Cello on 'Why Does It Always Rain On Me?' by Clea Friend
12-string Rickenbacker on 'There She Goes' kindly loaned by Bob Wooton

Your Guarantee of Quality

As publishers, we strive to produce
every book to the highest commercial standards.
The music has been freshly engraved and the book has
been carefully designed to minimise awkward page turns
and to make playing from it a real pleasure.
Particular care has been given to specifying acid-free,
neutral-sized paper made from pulps which have not been
elemental chlorine bleached. This pulp is from farmed
sustainable forests and was produced with
special regard for the environment.
Throughout, the printing and binding have been planned
to ensure a sturdy, attractive publication which
should give years of enjoyment.
If your copy fails to meet our high standards,
please inform us and we will gladly replace it.

www.musicsales.com

Music Sales' complete catalogue describes thousands of titles
and is available in full colour sections by subject, direct from
Music Sales Limited. Please state your areas of interest
and send a cheque/postal order for £1.50 for postage to:
Music Sales Limited, Newmarket Road,
Bury St. Edmunds, Suffolk IP33 3YB.

guitars, effects and set-up

Arthur Dick describes his recording techniques for the accompanying CD

angels

The lead part was played on a Tom Anderson guitar (rhythm pickups) fed into a Line 6 POD with a clean British Classic amp setting. For the solo, the lead pickups were switched in and the drive cranked up with the following settings: Drive: 9. Bass: 1. Mid: 1. Treble: 9. Reverb: off (add on mix). Taylor and Yamaha acoustics (stereo) provide additional weight to the rhythm section from verse two as well as two electric slide guitar (bottleneck) tracks played using a Strat and the POD's 'Brit Blues' (Marshall) and 'Small Tweed' (Fender) amp sounds... and a brass bottleneck of course!

lovefool

The organ/synth feature through the verses was doubled on a Gibson 345 with its tone rolled off via the tone selector and a Small Tweed amp from the POD giving a clean tight sound. Two bars before the choruses, distortion was kicked in by turning up the drive setting before returning to a clean funky rhythm sound for the chorus.
Additional harmony parts were played on a 1970s Telecaster, while the fuzz solo guitar in the background came from the Tom Anderson but with the POD's output fed into an Yamaha SPX1000 using a distortion preset that sounds like an electric razor!

road rage

An 'autowah' preset from a TC Electronic 'G-Force' effects was used with the Gibson 345 through the verses and a 'Brit Blues' setting from the POD: Drive: 3. Bass/Mid: 1. Treble: 8. Comp: 3. For the choruses and solo, the autowah was switched out and the drive (and therefore distortion) increased. Through the choruses the rhythm was tracked using the 345 with a different tone selected (that selector switch again!)

sit down

Two basic rhythm tracks were played on the Taylor and Yamaha acoustics miked with a Neumann U87 and AKG414. The lead part was played on the Gibson 345 through a MesaBoogie TriAxis Preamp with a little TC Electronic chorus added from the G-Force. A further guitar part (Gtr. 2) came from the Telecaster/POD's 'Brit Blues' amp combination.

there's no other way

It's Telecasters all the way! The Lead (left channel) was played using the rhythm (neck) pickup with the POD's 'Rectified' amp selected. The tracked second guitar (right channel) switched to the lead pickup and a 'Brit Blues' amp. The backward guitar solo was recorded on the digital 'Protools' system in the studio by reversing the track and playing along!

there she goes

The Taylor and Yamaha acoustics again provide a driving rhythm track together with the Gibson 345 using a slightly crunchy sound from the POD's 'Tweed Blues' (Fender) amp. The lead part was played on a 1967 12-string Rickenbaker (360/12) and the POD's 'Tweed Blues' amp.

why does it always rain on me?

A similar rhythm track to above using the combination of tracked acoustics and electric, the latter using the POD's 'Black Panel' amp (Fender) with a modest drive setting. The lead part again was played on the 345 but with a clean 'Brit Blues' sound and more compression.

what can i do

The Gibson 345, with its tone rolled off via the tone selector, was used along with an extreme amount of compression from the TC G-Force and a Focusrite Red 3! A 'Small Tweed' setting from the POD provided the amp sound (with no drive).

guitar tablature explained

Guitar music can be notated three different ways: on a musical stave, in tablature, and in rhythm slashes

RHYTHM SLASHES are written above the stave. Strum chords in the rhythm indicated. Round noteheads indicate single notes.

THE MUSICAL STAVE shows pitches and rhythms and is divided by lines into bars. Pitches are named after the first seven letters of the alphabet.

TABLATURE graphically represents the guitar fingerboard. Each horizontal line represents a string, and each number represents a fret.

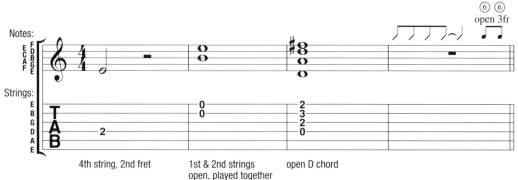

4th string, 2nd fret   1st & 2nd strings open, played together   open D chord

definitions for special guitar notation

SEMI-TONE BEND: Strike the note and bend up a semi-tone (1/2 step).

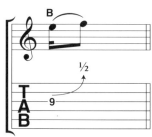

WHOLE-TONE BEND: Strike the note and bend up a whole-tone (whole step).

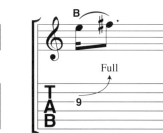

GRACE NOTE BEND: Strike the note and bend as indicated. Play the first note as quickly as possible.

QUARTER-TONE BEND: Strike the note and bend up a 1/4 step.

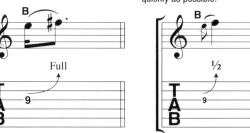

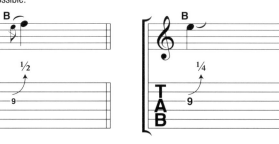

BEND & RELEASE: Strike the note and bend up as indicated, then release back to the original note.

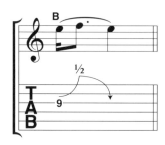

COMPOUND BEND & RELEASE: Strike the note and bend up and down in the rhythm indicated.

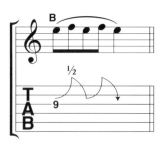

PRE-BEND: Bend the note as indicated, then strike it.

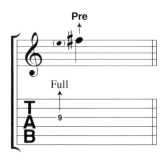

PRE-BEND & RELEASE: Bend the note as indicated. Strike it and release the note back to the original pitch.

UNISON BEND: Strike the two notes simultaneously and bend the lower note up to the pitch of the higher.

BEND & RESTRIKE: Strike the note and bend as indicated then restrike the string where the symbol occurs.

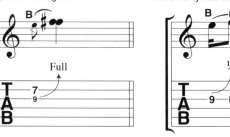

BEND, HOLD AND RELEASE: Same as bend and release but hold the bend for the duration of the tie.

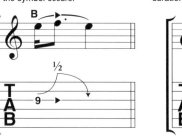

BEND AND TAP: Bend the note as indicated and tap the higher fret while still holding the bend.

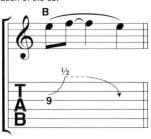

VIBRATO: The string is vibrated by rapidly bending and releasing the note with the fretting hand.

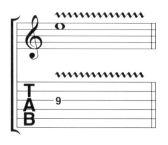

HAMMER-ON: Strike the first (lower) note with one finger, then sound the higher note (on the same string) with another finger by fretting it without picking.

PULL-OFF: Place both fingers on the notes to be sounded, Strike the first note and without picking, pull the finger off to sound the second (lower) note.

LEGATO SLIDE (GLISS): Strike the first note and then slide the same fret-hand finger up or down to the second note. The second note is not struck.

NOTE: The speed of any bend is indicated by the music notation and tempo.

SHIFT SLIDE (GLISS & RESTRIKE): Same as legato slide, except the second note is struck.

TRILL: Very rapidly alternate between the notes indicated by continuously hammering on and pulling off.

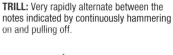

TAPPING: Hammer ("tap") the fret indicated with the pick-hand index or middle finger and pull off to the note fretted by the fret hand.

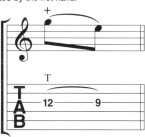

PICK SCRAPE: The edge of the pick is rubbed down (or up) the string, producing a scratchy sound.

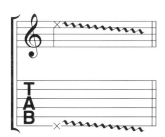

MUFFLED STRINGS: A percussive sound is produced by laying the fret hand across the string(s) without depressing, and striking them with the pick hand.

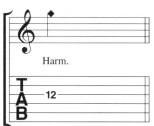

NATURAL HARMONIC: Strike the note while the fret-hand lightly touches the string directly over the fret indicated.

Harm.

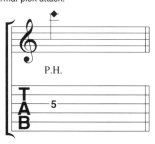

PINCH HARMONIC: The note is fretted normally and a harmonic is produced by adding the edge of the thumb or the tip of the index finger of the pick hand to the normal pick attack.

P.H.

HARP HARMONIC: The note is fretted normally and a harmonic is produced by gently resting the pick hand's index finger directly above the indicated fret (in parentheses) while the pick hand's thumb or pick assists by plucking the appropriate string.

H.H.

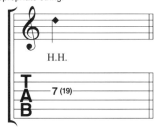

PALM MUTING: The note is partially muted by the pick hand lightly touching the string(s) just before the bridge.

P.M.

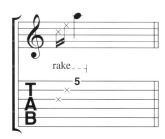

RAKE: Drag the pick across the strings indicated with a single motion.

rake

TREMOLO PICKING: The note is picked as rapidly and continuously as possible.

ARPEGGIATE: Play the notes of the chord indicated by quickly rolling them from bottom to top.

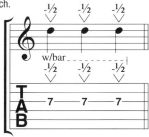

SWEEP PICKING: Rhythmic downstroke and/or upstroke motion across the strings.

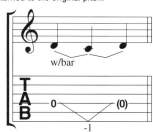

VIBRATO DIVE BAR AND RETURN: The pitch of the note or chord is dropped a specific number of steps (in rhythm) then returned to the original pitch.

w/bar

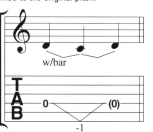

VIBRATO BAR SCOOP: Depress the bar just before striking the note, then quickly release the bar.

w/bar

VIBRATO BAR DIP: Strike the note and then immediately drop a specific number of steps, then release back to the original pitch.

w/bar

additional musical definitions

(accent)	•	Accentuate note (play it louder).
(accent)	•	Accentuate note with great intensity.
(staccato)	•	Shorten time value of note.
	•	Downstroke
V	•	Upstroke

D.%. al Coda

D.C. al Fine

tacet

1.   2.

• Go back to the sign (%), then play until the bar marked *To Coda* ⊕ then skip to the section marked ⊕ *Coda*.

• Go back to the beginning of the song and play until the bar marked *Fine* (end).

• Instrument is silent (drops out).

• Repeat bars between signs.

• When a repeated section has different endings, play the first ending only the first time and the second ending only the second time.

NOTE: Tablature numbers in parentheses mean:
1. The note is sustained, but a new articulation (such as hammer on or slide) begins.
2. A note may be fretted but not necessarily played.

angels

Words & Music by Robbie Williams & Guy Chambers

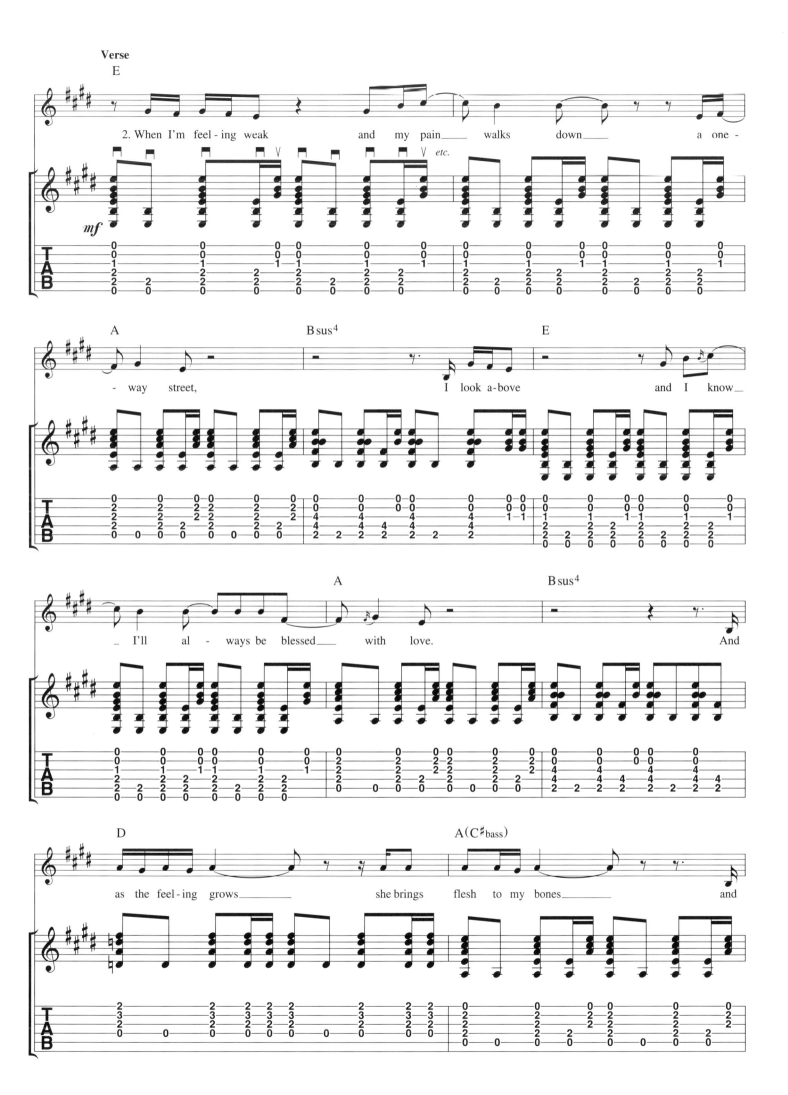

Verse

2. When I'm feel-ing weak   and   my pain___   walks   down___   a one-

- way   street,   I look a-bove   and I know___

___ I'll al - ways be blessed___ with   love.   And

as the feel-ing grows___   she brings   flesh   to my bones___   and

9

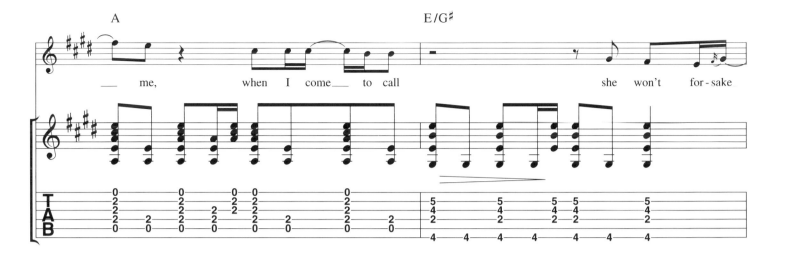

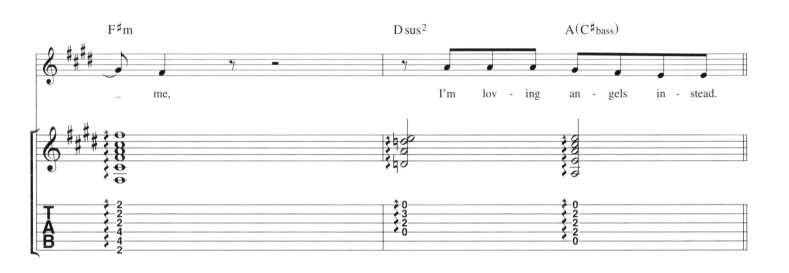

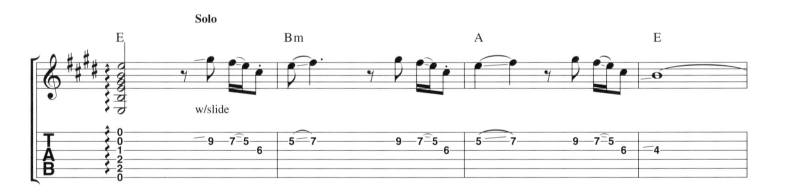

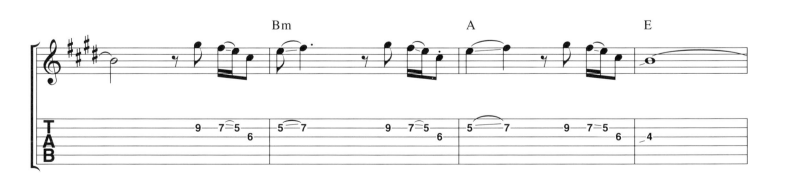

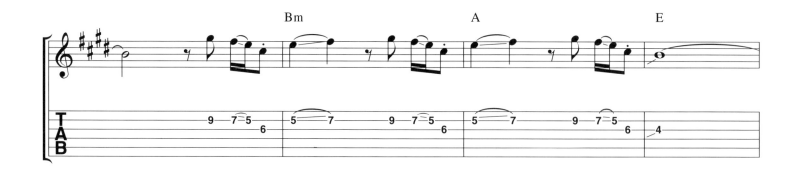

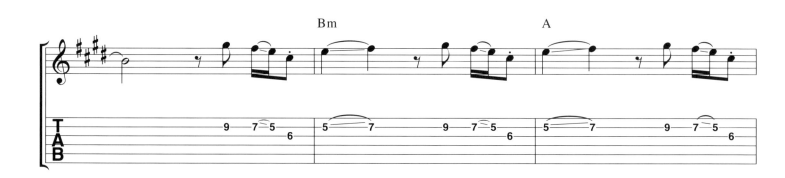

Chorus

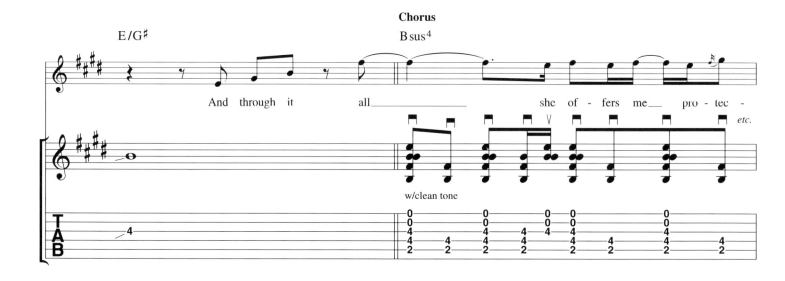

And through it all_____ she of - fers me__ pro - tec -

w/clean tone

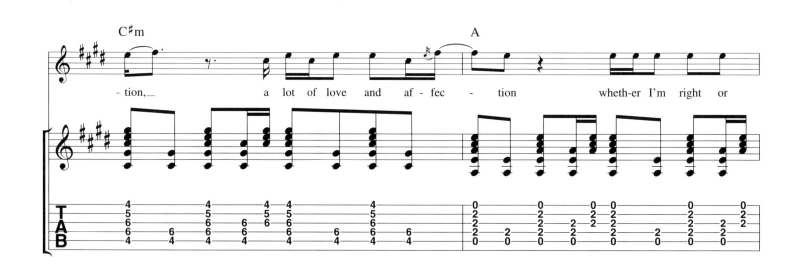

- tion,__ a lot of love and af - fec - tion wheth-er I'm right or

lovefool

Words & Music by Peter Svensson & Nina Persson

* play percussively, constant semiquaver rhythm

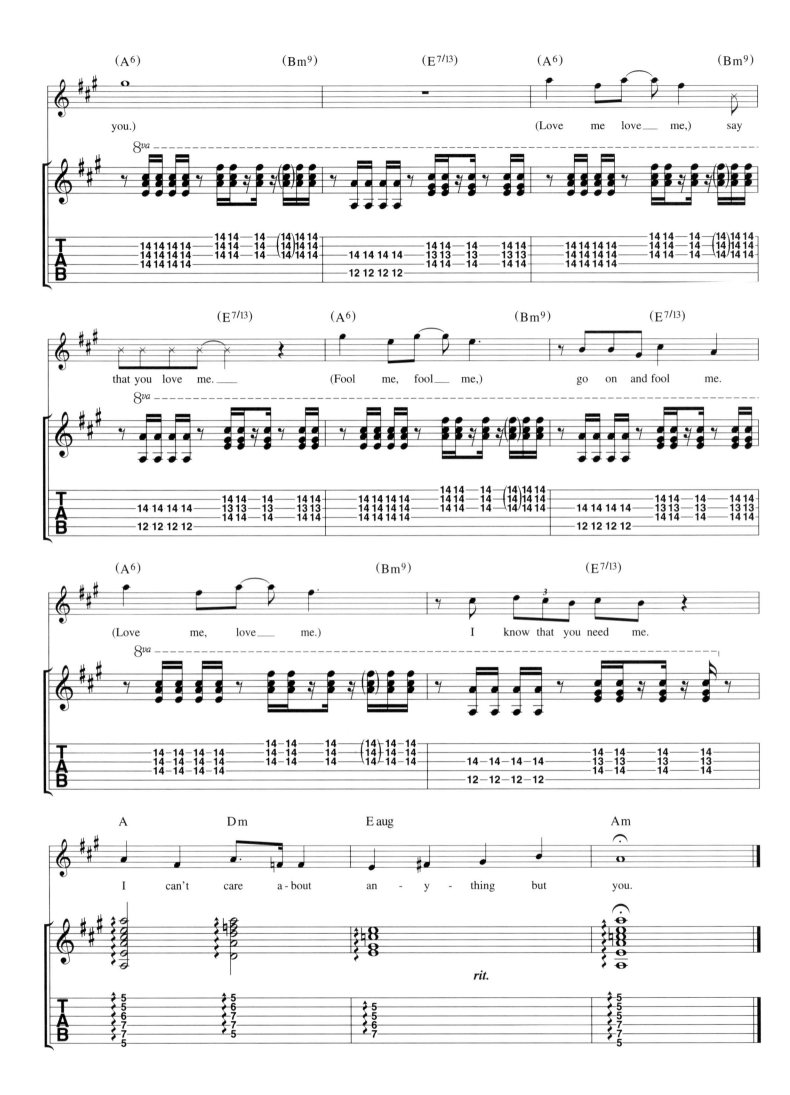

road rage

Words & Music by Cerys Matthews, Mark Roberts, Aled Richards, Paul Jones & Owen Powell

sit down

Words & Music by Tim Booth, Larry Gott, Gavan Whelan & Jim Glennie

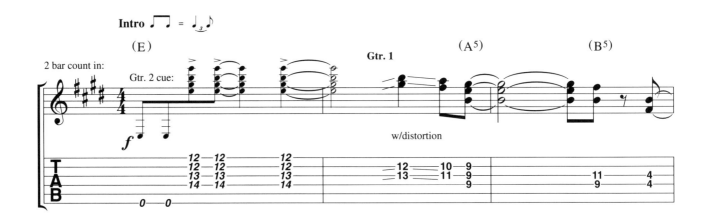

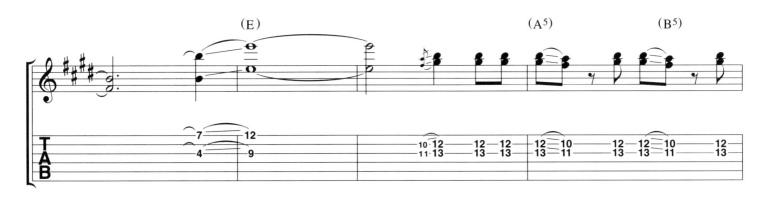

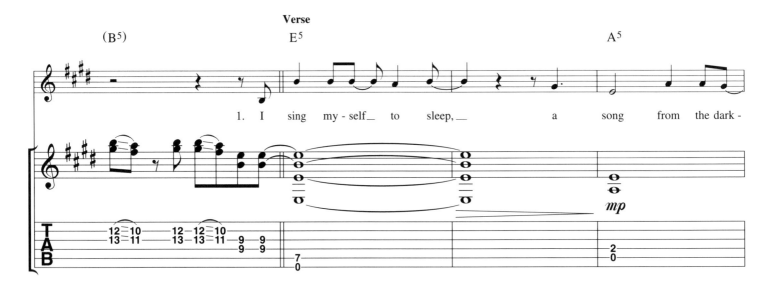

1. I sing my-self to sleep, a song from the dark-

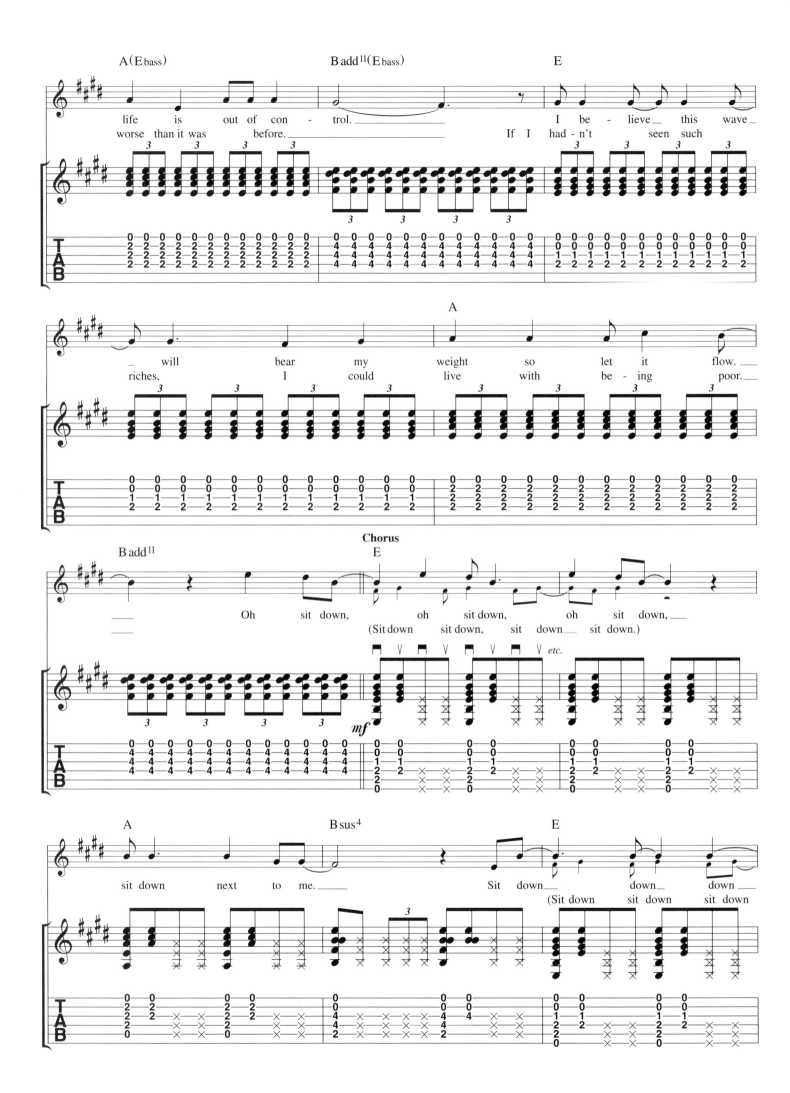

play guitar with...
all these

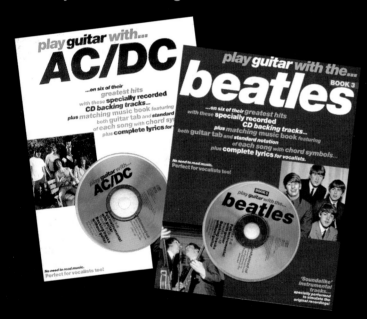

top bands and artists

play guitar with...
oasis
...on seven of their greatest hits
with these **specially recorded**
CD backing tracks...
plus matching music book featuring
both **guitar tab** and **standard notation**
of each song with chord symbols...
plus **complete lyrics** for vocalists

Seven great songs from
'Definitely Maybe' and
'What's The Story?'

No need to read music.
Perfect for vocalists too!

play guitar with...
the stone roses
BOOK 2
...on six of their
greatest hits
with these **specially recorded**
CD backing tracks...
plus matching music book featuring
both **guitar tab** and **standard notation**
of each song with chord symbols...
plus **complete lyrics** for vocalists

'Soundalike'
instrumental
tracks...
specially performed
to simulate the
original recordings

play guitar with...
paul weller
...on eight of his greatest hits
with these **specially recorded**
CD backing tracks...
plus matching music book featuring
both **guitar tab** and **standard notation**
of each song with chord symbols...
plus **complete lyrics** for vocalists.

'Soundalike'
instrumental
tracks...
specially performed
to simulate the
original recordings.

No need to read music.
Perfect for vocalists too!

play guitar with...
the 70's
...on eight great hits from ac/dc,
derek and the dominoes, dire straits,
the eagles, free, slade, thin lizzy and wings
with these **specially recorded**
CD backing tracks...
plus matching music book
of each song with chord symbols
plus complete lyrics for vocalists

'Soundalike'
instrumental
tracks...
specially performed
to simulate the
original recordings

play guitar with...
the 90's
...on seven great hits from eric clapton,
manic street preachers, metallica,
alanis morissette, oasis, pulp and the seahorses
with these **specially recorded**
CD backing tracks...
plus matching music book featuring
both **guitar tab** and **standard notation**
of each song with chord symbols...
plus **complete lyrics** for vocalists...

'Soundalike'
instrumental
tracks...
specially performed
to simulate the
original recordings

No need to read music.
Perfect for vocalists too!

bob marley
includes:
i shot the sheriff
jamming
no woman, no cry
Order No. AM937739

metallica
includes:
enter sandman
fade to black
the unforgiven
Order No. AM92559

metallica book 2
includes:
creeping death
seek and destroy
whiskey in the jar
Order No. AM955977

alanis morissette
includes:
hand in my pocket
ironic
you oughta know
Order No. AM943723

oasis
includes:
cigarettes & alcohol
morning glory
supersonic
Order No. AM935330

ocean colour scene
includes:
the circle
the day we caught the train
the riverboat song
Order No. AM943712

elvis presley
includes:
all shook up
blue suede shoes
hound dog
Order No. AM937090

pulp
includes:
common people
disco 2000
sorted for e's & wizz
Order No. AM938124

the rolling stones
includes:
brown sugar
(i can't get no) satisfaction
jumpin' jack flash
Order No. AM90247

sting
includes:
an englishman in
new york
fields of gold
if you love somebody
set them free
Order No. AM928092

the stone roses
includes:
i am the resurrection
i wanna be adored
ten storey love song
Order No. AM943701

the stone roses
book 2
includes:
fool's gold
love spreads
one love
Order No. AM955890

suede
includes:
animal nitrate
electricity
we are the pigs
Order No. AM955955

paul weller
includes:
the changingman
out of the sinking
wild wood
Order No. AM937827

the who
includes:
i can see for miles
pinball wizard
substitute
Order No. AM955867

the 60's
includes:
all along the watchtower
(jimi hendrix)
born to be wild
(steppenwolf)
not fade away
(the rolling stones)
Order No. AM957748

the 70's
includes:
all right now (free)
hotel california
(the eagles)
live and let die (wings)
Order No. AM957759

the 80's
includes:
addicted to love
(robert palmer)
need you tonight (inxs)
where the streets have
no name (U2)
Order No. AM957760

the 90's
includes:
everything must go
(manic street preachers)
love is the law (the seahorses)
wonderwall (oasis)
Order No. AM957770

play guitar with...

sample the whole series with these special compilations...

the gold book

the gold book
play guitar with...
...on eight great hits from **dire straits, the beatles, chuck berry, elvis presley, the kinks, eric clapton, john lennon** and **john lee hooker**
with these **specially recorded CD backing tracks...**
plus matching music book featuring both guitar tab and standard notation of each song with chord symbols complete lyrics for vocalists

'Soundalike' instrumental tracks... specially performed to simulate the original recordings

the platinum book

the platinum book
play guitar with...
...on seven great hits from **kula shaker, manic street preachers, ocean colour scene, oasis, stone roses, pulp** and **paul weller**
with these **specially recorded CD backing tracks...**
plus matching music book featuring both guitar tab and standard notation of each song with chord symbols...
plus complete lyrics for vocalists

'Soundalike' instrumental tracks... specially performed to simulate the original recordings

play guitar with... the **platinum** book
Tracks 1-7 Full instrumental with guitar Backing tracks without guitar
Enhanced CD

No need to read music.
Perfect for vocalists too!

the gold book
includes eight classic tracks:
jailhouse rock (elvis presley)
johnny b. goode (chuck berry)
layla (eric clapton)
sultans of swing (dire straits)
the healer (john lee hooker)
ticket to ride (the beatles)
woman (john lennon)
you really got me (the kinks)
Order No. AM951907

the platinum book
includes seven great songs:
*a design for life
   (manic street preachers)*
cigarettes & alcohol (oasis)
disco 2000 (pulp)
elephant stone (stone roses)
govinda (kula shaker)
the changingman (paul weller)
*the riverboat song
   (ocean colour scene)*
Order No. AM951918

Arthur Dick has transcribed the music and provided the recorded guitar parts for most of the titles in the **play guitar with...** series, often bringing in other professional specialist musicians to achieve the most authentic sounds possible!

A session guitarist with over twenty years' experience, he has worked with Cliff Richard, Barbara Dickson, Helen Shapiro, Bernie Flint and Chris Rea among others.

Arthur has played in many West End stage shows, and is in regular demand as a session player for TV, radio, and advertising productions.

He currently lectures on jazz and contemporary guitar at University Goldsmith's College, and works as a freelance production consultant.

Available from all good music retailers or, in case of difficulty, contact:

Music Sales Limited
Newmarket Road,
Bury St. Edmunds,
Suffolk IP33 3YB.
telephone 01284 725725
fax 01284 702592

www.musicsales.com

PUB04634

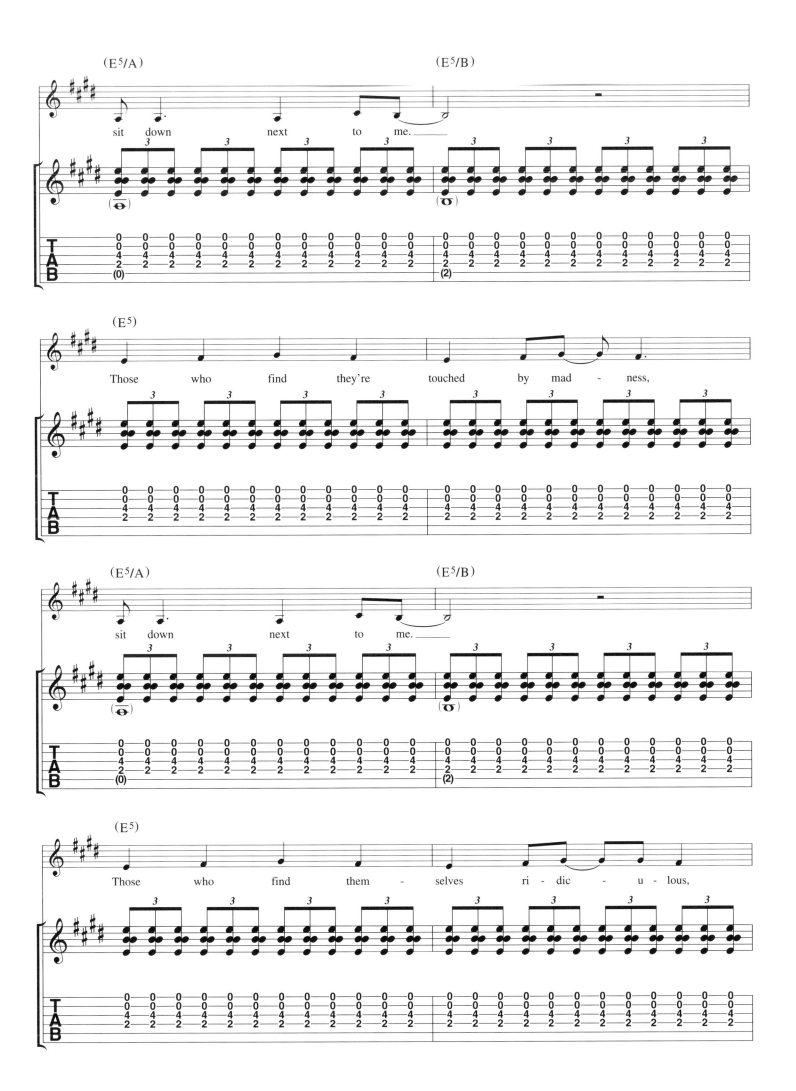

there's no other way

Words & Music by Damon Albarn, Alex James, Graham Coxon & Dave Rowntree

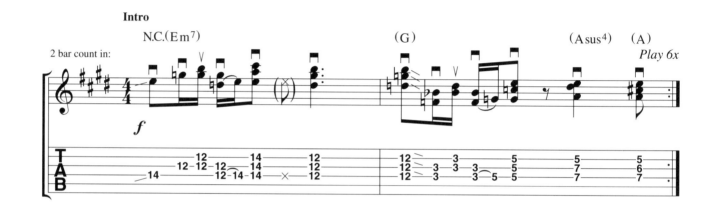

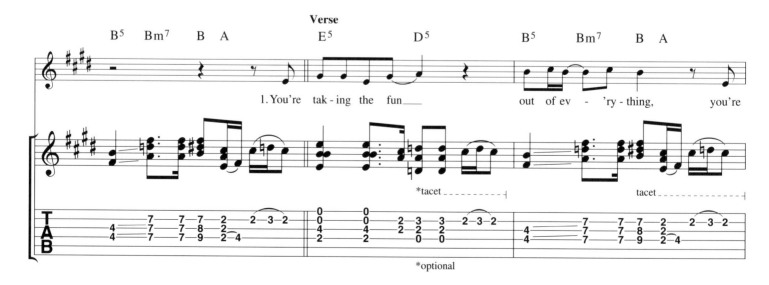

1. You're tak-ing the fun____ out of ev - 'ry-thing, you're

*optional

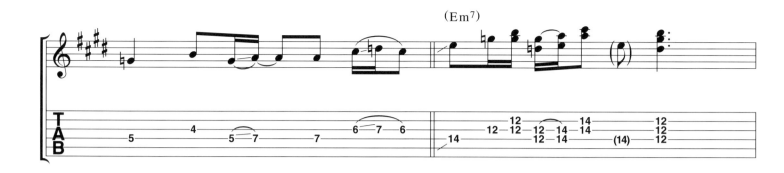

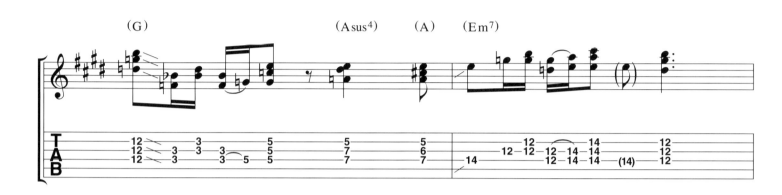

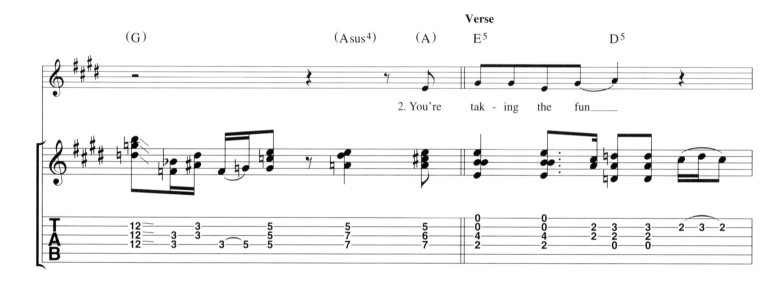

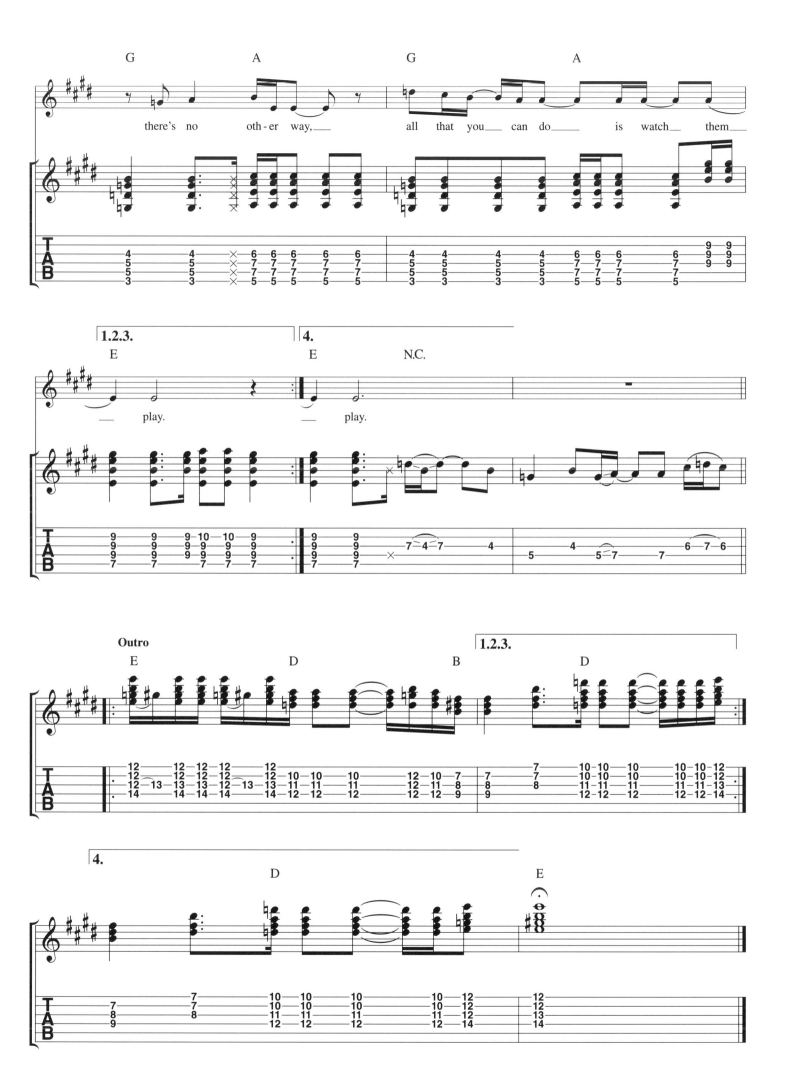

there's no oth-er way,___ all that you___ can do___ is watch___ them___

1.2.3.   4.

— play.   — play.

there she goes

Words & Music by Lee Mavers

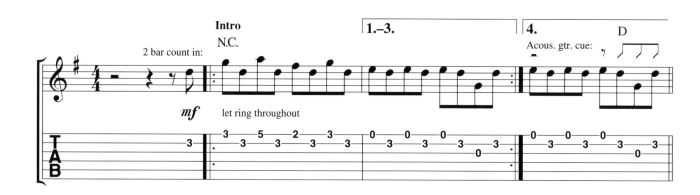

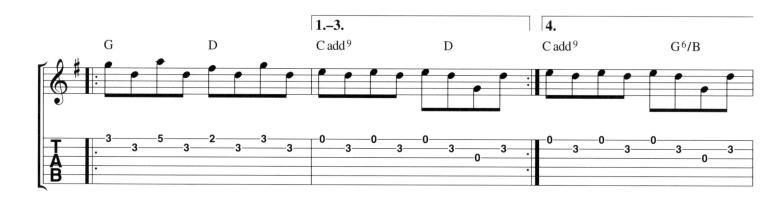

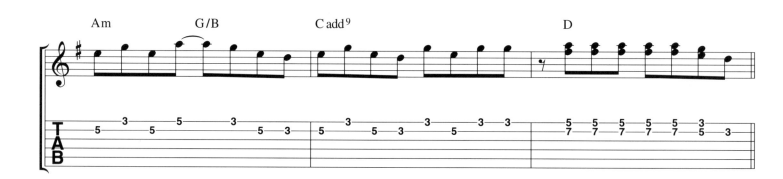

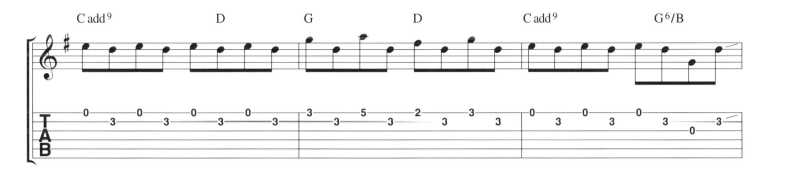

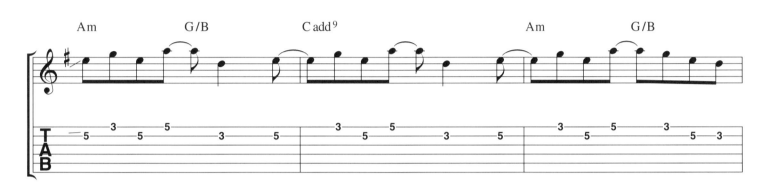

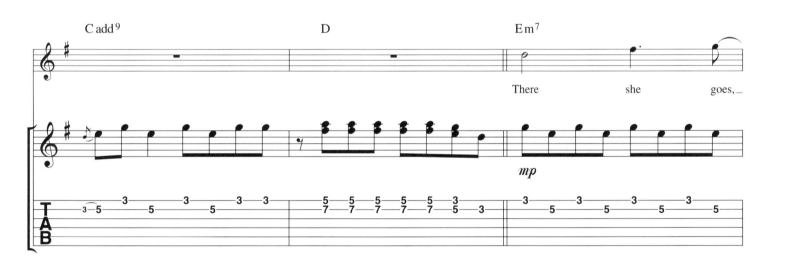

There she goes, __

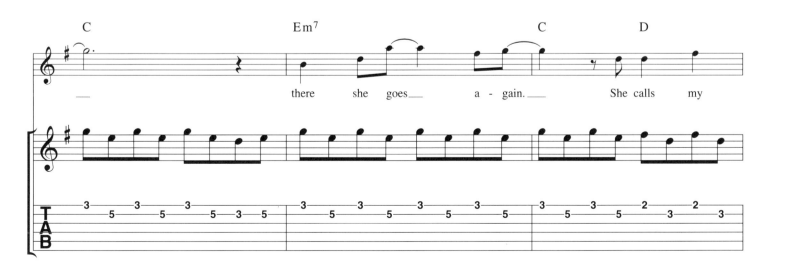

__ there she goes __ a - gain. __ She calls my

why does it always rain on me?

Words & Music by Fran Healy

Intro

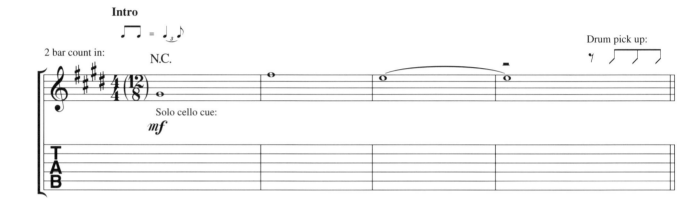

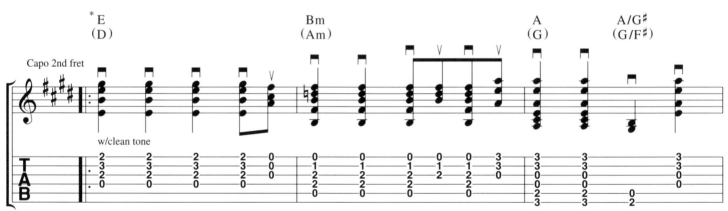

* Symbols in parentheses represent chord names with respect to capoed gtr. (Tab 0 = 2nd fret)
  Symbols above represent actual sounding chords.

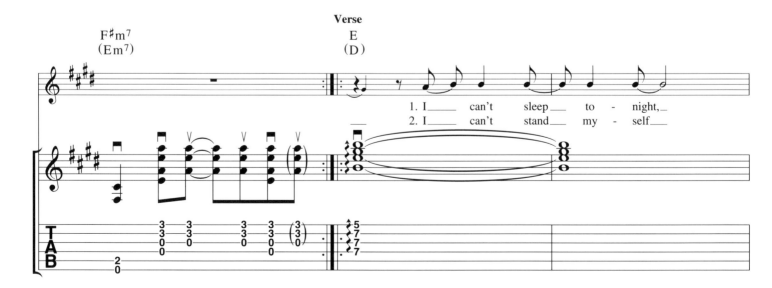

Chorus

Why__ does it al - ways rain__ on__ me? Is it be - cause__ I lied__ when I was sev - en - teen?__

Why__ does it al - ways rain__ on__ me? Ev - en when the sun is shin - ing,

I can't a - void__ the light - 'ning.__ I can't a - void__ the light - 'ning. Oh,__

48

what can i do

Words & Music by Andrea Corr, Caroline Corr, Sharon Corr & Jim Corr

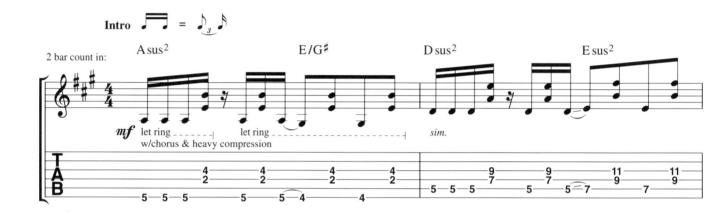

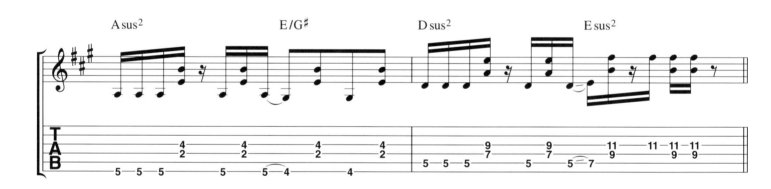

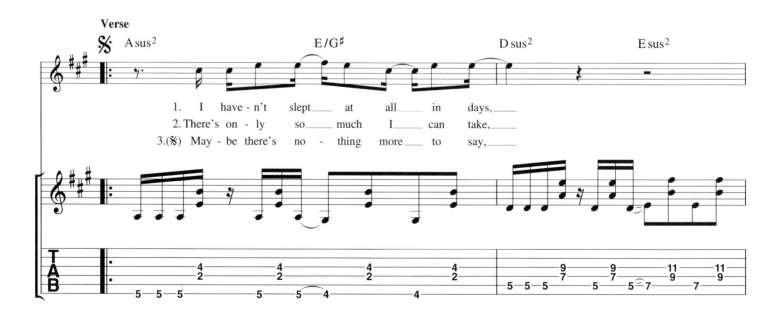

it's been so long___ since we___ have talked.
and I just got___ to let___ it go.
and in a fun - ny way___ I'm calm.

And I have been___ here ma - ny times,___
And who knows___ I might feel bet - ter,___ yeah,___
Be - cause the pow - er is not___ mine,___

Fig 1 . . .

I just don't know___ what I'm do - ing wrong.___
If I don't try and I don't hope.___
I'm just gon - na let it fly.

. . . end Fig 1